The Best Trick

by Rebecca Lewis
Illustrated by Camille Farr

Table of Contents

Illustrations by Camille Farr.
Cover design and interior illustration updated by Dave Lilly.
This edition, with modified layout, is published by Avyx, Inc., 2008.

Published by
Avyx, Inc.
8032 South Grant Way
Littleton, CO 80122-2705
(303) 483-0140 FAX (303) 483-0141
E-Mail: info@avyx.com

ISBN 978-1-887840-89-7

Jill's Pets

Jill has lots of pets.

She has a pet pig.

She has a red hen.

She has a little pup and a cat.

Her pets can do tricks.

Bill's Pets

Bill has lots of pets, too.

He has a duck

and a little red bug.

But his best pet

is his big dog, Bob.

Bill's pets can do tricks, too.

Do you have lots of pets?

Can your pets do tricks?

Pig Tricks

Jill's pig has a hut in a pen.

The pig has lots of mud

and a big log.

He can step on the log

and jump in the mud.

He has lots of fun!

But the pig is a mess

and he smells.

Jill said, “My pig’s trick

is the best trick!”

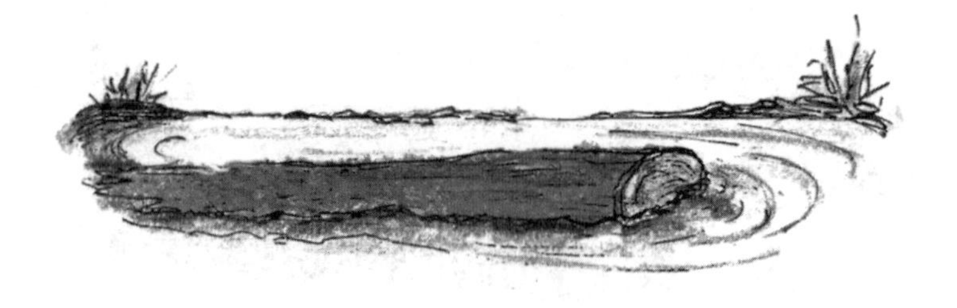

Is Jill’s pig’s trick the best trick?

Duck Tricks

Bill said, “My duck has the best trick. My duck can jump in the pond and swim fast.

“If he gets to the mud, he can step on the mud and not get stuck or slip.

"He is not a mess, but he can

have lots of fun!

"My duck's trick is the best trick!"

The duck has a good trick.

But is the duck's trick

the best trick?

Cat Tricks

Jill said, "No, Bill. The duck has a good trick, but my cat's trick is the best.

"I can drag a rag and the cat will run and jump and grab the rag. I run fast and pull on the rag, but my cat still wins!

"She gets the rag, drags it
to her bed, and puts it in.
Then she naps on it and
purrs and purrs.

"That is the best pet trick!"

Is the cat's trick the best trick yet?

Big Dog Tricks

Bill grins at Jill.

“Your cat can do a good trick,”

he says, “and my little red bug

cannot do a good trick.

“But my dog can do

a lot of good tricks.

If I toss a twig, my dog can run

and jump up and grab it!

“He can run fast in the grass.

He can run as fast

as a fox and not slip!

“He can swim in the pond

or grab a rag if I drag it.

"He can jump off a log

into the mud.

"He can do the best tricks.

My dog wins!"

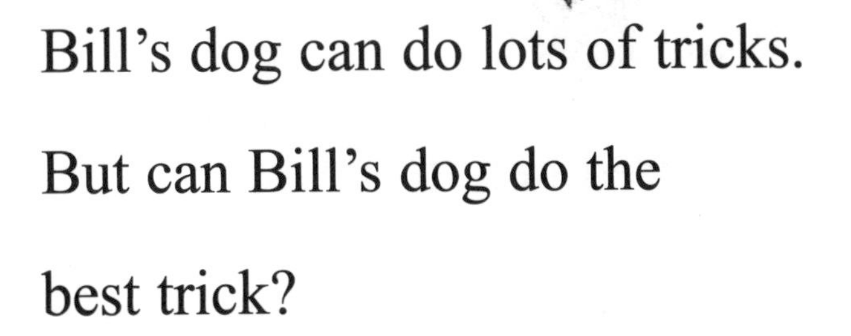

Bill's dog can do lots of tricks.

But can Bill's dog do the

best trick?

The Best Trick

Jill looks at her pup.

"My pup is still little,"

she says. "But my pup

will do big dog tricks

when he gets big."

Bill grins. "My dog wins," he says.

Jill looks at her pets.

"No," she says.

"I have a red hen, too.

You will see.

My red hen will win.

Her trick is the best trick!"

"Your red hen cannot win,"

says Bill. "Your hen cannot swim.

She cannot run as

fast as a fox.

She cannot jump

and grab a rag, or

purr in her bed.

What trick can

a hen do?"

Jill grins at Bill. "I will tell you,"

she says.

The Red Hen's Trick

"My hen cannot swim or jump or grab or purr," says Jill.

"But my hen has a nest.

When she sits on her nest, she drops eggs into her nest.

Then she sits and sits on her eggs.

At last the eggs start to crack.

Then the little chicks look up

to get fed.

"Come and look in the hen's nest

and you will see.

My hen has six little chicks.

Eggs into little chicks

is the best trick!"

Bill looks at Bob, then

he looks at the hen

and the chicks.

"Yes," says Bill. "That trick is

the best trick. Your hen wins!"

Chicks for Bill

Bill looks at the six chicks
in the nest.
"May I have one of the chicks?"
he asks. "I do not have a chick
or a hen."

Jill looks at the chicks.
"This chick is too little,"
she says. "That chick is
too little as well.

"No, you cannot have a chick."

Jill looks at Bill.

Bill is sad.

Jill grins.

"But the chicks will get big fast!"

she says.

"When the chicks

are big, you may

have a chick."

Bill is not sad.

He is glad.

"Thank you, Jill," he says.

"I will come back and

get a chick when they are big!"

The Chicks Get Big

The chicks are still little and just sit in the nest.

The red hen looks for bugs and seeds to get for them. The chicks need a lot of bugs and seeds.

The hen must feed the chicks so they will get big fast.

As the chicks get big,

they can see from the nest.

They look at the hen hut.

They see the dirt and the grass.

They see the mud and the pig's hut.

They do not see the hen.

The chicks are big and do not want

to just sit in the nest.

They want to be in the grass

and look for bugs.

No Bugs

The chicks want to get

bugs and seeds.

They see seeds on the dirt

of the hen hut.

One by one they jump from

the nest on to the dirt.

The hen is not in the hut.

She went to look

for bugs.

The chicks want to look for bugs, too. They do not see bugs in the dirt of the hut so they go to look for bugs in the grass.

The grass is green and soft, but the chicks do not see bugs in the grass.

The cat is in the grass, too, and she sees the chicks.

A Good Snack

The chicks need a snack,

but they do not see bugs

in the green grass.

They look at the pig's pen.

There are lots of bugs

in the pig's pen.

The cat hides in the grass

to see the chicks.

The chicks run to the

pig's pen to get the bugs.

The cat sees the chicks run,

so she runs, too.

The chicks want the bugs for

a snack, but the cat wants

the chicks for a snack!

A Mad Pig

The chicks jump into the pig's pen.

The cat can jump into the

pig's pen, too.

But the pig is big and the pen

is full of mud.

The cat looks at the pig.

She looks at the mud.

It is not fun to get stuck
in the mud! Nor is it fun
to get a big pig mad.

The cat sits on the
grass by the pig pen.
The chicks will come back.

In the Pig Pen

The chicks run on the mud

in the pig pen.

They are little, so they do not slip.

They do not get stuck in the mud,

but a little mud sticks to them!

They look for bugs in the mud.

They see lots of bugs by the log.

They run and jump to get bugs.

The pig is in his hut but sees the chicks in his pen.

The cat on the grass sees the chicks get bugs, too.

They peep and peep as they feed

on the bugs.

The pig is not mad,

but he grunts and stamps.

He wants the chicks to go.

The chicks bump into the log

and run back to the grass.

The Hen

The hen gets back to the hen hut.

She looks for her chicks in the nest, but they are not there.

She runs fast to look for them. She looks for them in the hut but they are not there.

She looks for them in the grass,

but they are not there.

The hen sees the cat in the grass.

Then she sees her

chicks in the pig pen.

She sees that the cat will get

them when they come back.

When the pig stamps and grunts,

she sees the chicks start to run

back to the grass.

Help for the Chicks

The hen sees that the
chicks will run back
to where the cat is.

Her chicks must have help!

She runs fast and starts
to peck at the cat.

Jill sees that the chicks

are not in the nest.

When she sees the hen peck

at the cat, she runs fast

to help, too.

She grabs the cat.

The hen calls her chicks
from the pig's pen
and gets them to
run back to the nest.

The hen is cross with her chicks.
They are in the nest,
but they are wet with mud!

The Chicks are Big

Jill comes to help the hen.

She will get the mud off

the chicks.

She puts them in

a sink and gets

them wet.

They do not want

to get all wet!

Jill thinks, "The chicks are

not little. They are big.

“My hen hut is not big,

and I do not need six chicks.

Chicks are fun to have,

but six big chicks are a lot.

I will tell Bill to come

and get a chick.

“In fact, Bill can have two chicks.

My hen will be happy

with four chicks.”

Lots and Lots of Pets

Jill calls Bill.

"Come and get

a chick," she says.

"In fact, you may have two.

"Chicks are fun, but I need help.

The chicks are big.

Six big chicks are a lot."

Bill is so happy!

Bill comes to

get his chicks.

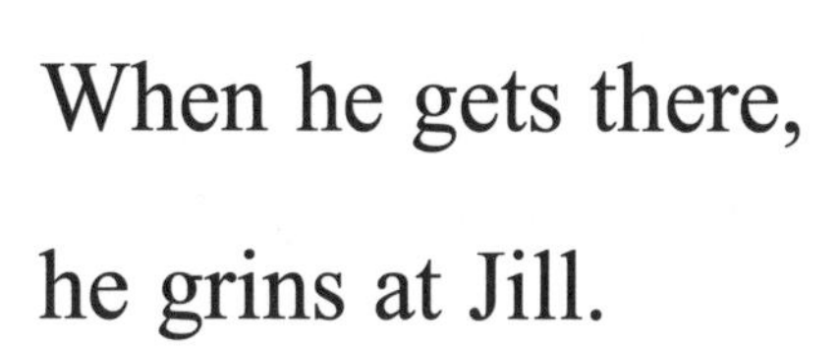

When he gets there,

he grins at Jill.

"I have these for you," he says.

He has two

little ducks

in his hand.

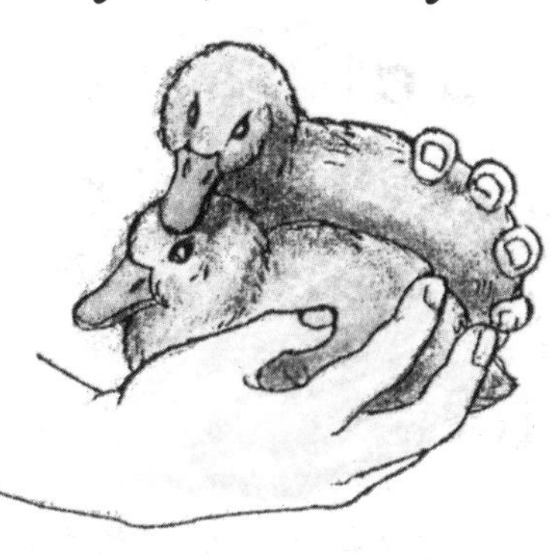

"My duck can do the same trick

your hen can," he says.

"It *is* the best trick!"

Jill grins back at Bill.

"Thank you," she says.

"I will have ducks and you will

have hens.

We will have lots and lots of pets!"